Effectiveness of Treatment in Reducing Drug-Related Crime

Report prepared for
The National Council for
Crime Prevention, Sweden

Brå – a centre of knowledge on crime and measures to combat crime

The Swedish National Council for Crime Prevention (Brottsförebyggande rådet – Brå) works to reduce crime and improve levels of safety in society by producing data and disseminating knowledge on crime and crime prevention work and the justice system's responses to crime.

Production:
Swedish Council for Crime Prevention, Information and publications,
Box 1386, 111 93 Stockholm.
Telephone +46(0)8 401 87 00, fax +46(0)8 411 90 75, e-mail info@bra.se
The National Council on the internet www.bra.se
Authors: Katy R. Holloway, Trevor H. Bennett, David P. Farrington
Cover illustration: Helena Halvarsson
Cover: Anna Gunneström
Printing: Edita Norstedts Västerås 2008
© Brottsförebyggande rådet 2008
ISBN 978-91-86027-12-4

Contents

Foreword

The principal objective of drug treatment programs is usually to reduce drug use. But do such programs also reduce crime? What does the research tell us?

There are never sufficient resources to conduct rigorous scientific evaluations of all the crime prevention measures employed in individual countries like Sweden. And to date the efforts devoted to high quality evaluations of drug treatment programs and their effects on crime in Sweden have been limited. For these reasons, the Swedish National Council for Crime Prevention (Brå) has commissioned renowned researchers to carry out an international review of the research published in this field.

This report presents a systematic review, including a statistical meta-analysis, of the effects of drug treatment programs on crime. The work has been carried out by Dr. Katy Holloway of the University of Glamorgan, Professor Trevor H. Bennett, also of the University of Glamorgan (United Kingdom), and Professor David P. Farrington of Cambridge University (United Kingdom), who have also written the report. The study follows the rigorous methodological requirements of a systematic review. The analysis combines the results from a large number of evaluations that are considered to satisfy a list of empirical criteria for measuring effects as reliably as possible. The analysis then uses the results from these previous evaluations to calculate and produce an overview of the effects that drug treatment programmes do and do not produce. Thus the objective is to systematically evaluate the results from a large number of studies from different countries in order to produce a more reliable picture of the opportunities and limitations associated with drug treatment programmes in relation to crime prevention efforts.

The systematic review, and the statistical meta-analysis, in this case build upon a large number of scientific evaluations from different part of the world, producing highly relevant findings on the effects of drug treatment programmes. Even though important questions remain unanswered, the study provides the most accessible and far-reaching overview to date of drug treatment programs and their effects on crime.

Stockholm, October 2008

Jan Andersson
Director-General

Summary

The majority of European countries have a drug strategy that aims to reduce drug-related crime. One of the methods commonly used for achieving this is to provide treatment for drug users. In most countries, treatment for drug users is available through conventional medical referral processes. In some countries, treatment is also made available from within the criminal justice system. This can be part of a referral process whereby offenders are diverted at various stages into treatment or treatment can be provided from within the criminal justice system as part of a prison programme. In order for the strategy to be effective, it needs to be demonstrated that treatment for drug misuse can lead to a reduction in crime.

This report presents the results of a systematic review of the literature on the effects of different kinds of intervention for problematic drug use on criminal behaviour. The main selection criteria were that the evaluation should be based on voluntary treatment programmes that aimed to reduce drug use (e.g. methadone maintenance, detoxification, or self-help programs) or criminal justice programmes that aimed to reduce drug use and drug-related crime (e.g. drug courts and drug testing programmes).

The main finding of the narrative review was that the majority of treatment programmes (68%) were associated with positive outcomes (the treatment group performed better than the comparison group in terms of subsequent criminal behaviour). In seven of the nine treatment categories investigated, the majority of evaluations produced positive findings. The most successful were psycho-social approaches and therapeutic communities. It was only in relation to other treatment programmes and other criminal justice system programmes that the percentage of positive outcomes fell below 50 per cent.

The main finding of the meta analysis was that the majority of studies investigated (25 of 37) showed a favourable effect on criminal behaviour. The mean effect size for all studies combined showed that the treatment groups were associated with a 26 per cent reduction in criminal behaviour compared with the comparison groups. Five of the seven programmes investigated generated effect sizes that showed a favourable impact of the programme on crime. The two most effective programmes measured by the meta analysis were therapeutic communities and supervision.

The report concludes that drug treatment programmes (especially psycho-social programmes and therapeutic communities) are effective in reducing criminal behaviour. However, the moderator analysis showed that there were statistically significant differences among programme types. It is difficult to explain the differences in effectiveness of programmes without a better understanding of the programme content and intensity. The main research implications of the report are that evaluations need to be of a high quality and to present their findings in a way that can be used in future meta analyses. The main implication for policy is that drug treatment can be effective in reducing criminal behaviour and is a useful means of reducing crime. However, more needs to be known about variations in effectiveness and the influence of programme type, intensity, and context on crime outcomes.

Acknowledgements

We would like to acknowledge the contribution of the UK Home Office in the production of the original report of the systematic review. We would also like to acknowledge the researchers who worked with us on the original review (Catherine Appleton, Steven Brown, Tracy Pitman, Jane Nolan) and the updated review (Hannah Gordon).

Katy R. Holloway
Trevor H. Bennett
David P. Farrington

I. Introduction

The majority of European countries have a drug strategy that aims to reduce drug-related crime. One of the methods commonly used for achieving this is to provide treatment for drug users. In some countries, treatment is available only through conventional medical referral. In other countries treatment is also made available as part of the criminal justice process. This latter kind usually comprises some kind of diversion from criminal justice processing into treatment or directly from within the criminal justice system as, for example, part of a prison programme. In order for the strategy to be effective, it needs to be demonstrated that treatment for drug misuse can lead to a reduction in crime. Hence, the research question considered in this report is, 'Does drug treatment lead to a reduction in offending?'.

The answer to this question is not obvious. In the first place, drug treatment programmes typically aim to reduce drug use not crime. It is not immediately clear how drug treatment might also reduce crime. In the second place, the evaluative research to date has produced mixed findings with some studies showing that programmes work while others showing that they do not work. The current report presents the findings of a systematic review of the literature which aimed to determine the extent to which drug treatment programmes were effective in reducing subsequent criminal behaviour.

The report is based on an updated and extended version of a systematic review conducted in 2004 for the UK Home Office. The original report included studies published up to the middle of 2004, whereas the current report includes studies published up to the middle of 2008. The original and updated reviews were both based on the methods adopted by the Campbell Collaboration Crime and Justice Group for conducting systematic reviews. Systematic reviews use rigorous methods for selecting relevant studies and for screening them for suitability for inclusion in the review. The methods used are detailed and transparent and should be replicable.

The report is divided into five main chapters. This first chapter is the introduction. The following chapter provides the background context for the research and discusses the findings of previous systematic reviews. The next chapter describes the methods used for conducting the systematic review and for selecting the studies for inclusion. The fourth chapter presents the results of the review, including the findings of both a narrative review and meta-analysis. The final chapter presents the conclusions to the research and draws out the policy and research implications of the findings.

II. Background

There have been many reviews of the literature on the effectiveness of drug treatment programmes (e.g. Chanhatasilpa, MacKenzie & Hickman, 2000; Hall, 1996; and Vaughn & Howard, 2004). However, most of these have investigated the effects of programmes on drug misuse. It is much less common for reviews to study the effects of programmes on other problem behaviours, such as criminal behaviour. This neglect of criminal behaviour is important as research has shown that the majority of drug misusers presenting to drug treatment programmes are self-reported offenders (Gossop, Marsden, Stewart & Kidd, 2003) and a notable proportion of these commit crimes at a high rate (Strang, Marsden, Cummins, Farrell, Finch, Gossop, Stewart & Welch, 2000). It has also been shown that drug-misusing offenders often continue to offend both during and after drug treatment (Hutchinson, Taylor, Gruer, Barr, Mills, Elliott, Goldberg, Scott & Gilchrist, 2000).

There have been some prior reviews of the literature that have included criminal behaviour as an outcome measure. Only a small number of these used meta-analytic techniques. In total, we found six systematic reviews that used meta-analysis to investigate the effect of drug-treatment programmes on criminal behaviour. Five were conducted in the USA and one in Italy. Three of the six reviews were based on single treatment programmes (Marsch, 1998; Kirchmayer, Davoli, Verster, Amato, Ferri and Perucci, 2002; and Wilson, Mitchell & MacKenzie, 2006) and three were based on multiple programmes (Prendergast, Podus, Chang & Urada, 2002; Mitchell, MacKenzie & Wilson, 2005; and Pearson & Lipton, 1998).

The three studies of single treatment programmes showed modest positive effect sizes for the treatment program. Marsch (1998) investigated the effectiveness of methadone maintenance programmes on various problem behaviours. Seventeen of the 24 studies providing results on criminal behaviour showed a positive and significant effect size ranging from r=0.01 to r=0.76, with a weighted mean of r=0.16. The mean effect size was greater for studies that examined drug-related crime (r=0.67) than those that examined drug- and property-related crime combined (r=0.14). Kirchmayer, Davoli, Verster, Amato, Ferri and Perucci (2002) explored the efficacy of naltrexone maintenance treatment in preventing relapse and reincarceration among opioid addicts. Two of the 14 studies included in the review provided results on criminal behaviour. The meta-analysis showed that use of naltrexone in addition to behavioural treatment significantly decreased the probability of re-incarceration during the study period (OR=0.30). Wilson, Mitchell and MacKenzie (2006) examined the results of 38 evaluations of drug courts that placed drug-misusing offenders in treatment programmes. The mean odds-ratio for all offence types was 1.71. The effect size was greater in relation to drug offences (1.68) compared with non-drug offences (1.29), and for juveniles (2.11) compared with adults (1.69).

The three studies based on multiple treatment modalities also indicated significant differences between the experimental and comparison groups. Prendergast et al. (2002) conducted a systematic review and meta-analysis of 25 studies that investigated the outcome of drug treatment on crime. The review included five treatment modalities: methadone maintenance programmes, therapeutic communities, outpatient drug-free programmes, detoxification programmes, and private sector treatment. Studies were eligible for inclusion if they were conducted in the United States, published between 1965 and 1996, and were based on adult drug abusers. Overall, the mean effect size for crime outcomes for all treatments combined was r=0.13. The authors concluded that drug treatment was effective in reducing criminal behaviour. However, there were no significant differences in effect sizes across treatment modalities.

Mitchell, MacKenzie and Wilson (2005) conducted a meta-analysis of 26 evaluations of incarceration-based drug treatment programmes. The study included evaluations of therapeutic communities, group counselling, boot camps, and methadone maintenance. The overall mean odds ratio for all programmes combined was 1.25, which represented a statistically significant reduction in post-treatment offending. However, there were some important differences in outcomes by programme type. Only therapeutic communities (OR=1.47) and group counselling programmes (OR=1.25) were associated with lower rates of offending. There was no difference in post-treatment offending between participants and non-participants in boot camps, and those in methadone maintenance programmes were significantly more likely than the comparison groups to offend following treatment. Pearson and Lipton (1998) also conducted a meta-analysis of incarceration-based drug-treatment programmes. They investigated six studies of boot camps and seven studies of drug-focused group counselling and concluded that neither was effective in reducing criminal behaviour. However, their analysis of seven studies of therapeutic communities concluded that these were effective (r=0.13).

The combined results of these six meta-analyses are far from conclusive. One of the three reviews of methadone treatment programmes concluded that it was associated with reduced offending (Marsch, 1998), one concluded that it resulted in higher rates of offending (Mitchell, MacKenzie & Wilson, 2005), and one found that its effect was positive, but no different from that of any other treatment modality (Prendergast et al., 2002). All three reviews of therapeutic communities concluded that they were effective in reducing offending (Pearson and Lipton, 1998; Mitchell, MacKenzie & Wilson, 2005; and Prendergast et al., 2002), although the latter reported that they were no more effective than other drug treatment methods. One of the two reviews that included group counselling concluded that it was effective in reducing recidivism (Mitchell, MacKenzie & Wilson, 2005) and the other reported that it was not effective (Pearson & Lipton, 1998). The one review that examined the effectiveness of naltrexone maintenance treatment in preventing crime (Kirchmayer et al. 2002) found that it was effective in reducing re-incarceration.

The main aim of the current review is to investigate the effectiveness of drug treatment programmes in reducing criminal behaviour. It adds to the work of previous meta-analyses by including drug treatment implemented in the UK and Europe, as well as the US, programmes initiated by the criminal justice system as well as through conventional routes, and more recent research covering modern versions of drug treatment.

III. Research methods

This report presents the results of a systematic review of the literature on the effects of different kinds of intervention for problematic drug use on criminal behaviour. Systematic reviews use rigorous methods for locating, analyzing, and collating evidence from a number of studies. They have explicit objectives and criteria for including or excluding studies and are based on extensive searches of the literature for eligible evaluations. They are also based on careful extraction and coding of key features of the studies and are sufficiently detailed to allow replication. Details of the methods of systematic reviews can be found in several publications (Welsh & Farrington, 2002; Farrington & Petrosino, 2000; Farrington & Welsh, 2002).

Criteria for inclusion

In selecting evaluations for inclusion in this review, three main criteria were used, concerning the type of intervention, the type of evaluation method used, and the type of outcome measures.

The main criteria relating to the type of intervention were that the evaluation should be based on either treatment programmes that aimed to reduce drug use (e.g. methadone maintenance or detoxification) or criminal justice programmes that aimed to reduce both drug use and drug-related crime (e.g. drug courts or drug testing programmes).

The criteria relating to the type of method used were that the evaluation should use methods of sufficient quality that could provide interpretable results. The current research broadly follows the methodological quality criteria adopted by Sherman, Gottfredson, MacKenzie, Reuter, Eck & Bushway (1997) in their version of the Scientific Methods Scale (SMS). The SMS is based on a five-point scale that ranks studies according to their ability to establish causality and to minimize threats to validity. Levels 1 and 2 are the lowest levels and include studies that seek to determine either a simple correlation at one point in time or differences between before and after measures over time without comparable control conditions. Levels 3 to 5 designs provide more robust findings and include studies that compare before and after measures for experimental and control conditions and evaluations based on random assignment to programme or control conditions. Evaluations are deemed eligible for inclusion in this review if they were at least Level 3 on the SMS scale (see also Farrington, 2003).

The main condition relating to outcome measures was that the study must include a measure of criminal behaviour. Studies that evaluated the effect of the intervention on drug use alone were excluded from the review. This was because the primary objective of the review was to investigate the effects of drug treatment programmes on crime.

Other selection criteria were that the evaluation was published in the English language and that the study was available during the period of the research. Studies were only included if they were published during the period between January 1980 and June 2008 when the selection component of the research was completed. The evaluation could be presented in any form and included reports, journal publications and other manuscripts.

Search methods

Evaluations were obtained mainly by searching online databases, reviewing citations in eligible studies, and contacting key researchers in the field. The databases included: Applied Social Sciences Index and Abstracts, Criminal Justice Abstracts, C2-SPECTR, International Bibliography of the Social Sciences, PsycARTICLES, PsycINFO, National Criminal Justice Reference Service, and the Home Office Research Development and Statistics publications database.

Each database was investigated using a list of predetermined search terms. Each search term yielded a list of titles and abstracts that were carefully reviewed. Studies that were clearly not evaluations of drug treatment programmes were removed from the list. Obtained studies were screened for eligibility using the inclusion criteria described above and relevant data from eligible studies were entered into the research database.

Attrition rates

The searches of the online databases resulted in a total of nearly 12,000 'hits'. The titles and abstracts of these studies were then checked for relevance. Studies that were not prima facie evaluations of drug treatment programmes were excluded at this point. This resulted in 701 studies selected from the searched databases. In addition, we already had in our possession, or selected from bibliographies, 80 further studies of possible relevance, making a total of 781 studies initially selected. Of these, 590 were obtained during the study period. The main reason for not obtaining publications was that the inter-library loan system was unable to locate them. The obtained studies were then checked for eligibility using the criteria mentioned above. This resulted in 75 eligible studies. The main reasons for exclusion were that the study was not an evaluation of a treatment programme or the SMS methods score was below Level 3. Thirty-seven of the 75 eligible studies presented sufficient information in their results to enable raw data to be extracted for the purpose of the meta-analysis.

Eligible studies

Details of the 75 studies included in the review are shown in Table 1. Most of the studies (53) were conducted in the USA. The others were conducted in the UK (15), Australia (4), Scotland (1), Sweden (1) and Switzerland (1). Nine of the studies were published in the 1980s, 28 in the 1990s and 38 in the 2000s. The majority of evaluations (48) employed a quasi-experimental research design in which pre- and post-test measures of crime were recorded for experimental and comparison groups. The remaining 27 studies recorded post-test only measures of crime among subjects who had been randomly allocated into experimental and comparison groups.

Most of the evaluations were based on a single treatment type and a single comparison group. When studies included multiple treatments, a random-selection procedure was used to identify the experimental program. The comparison condition was usually 'no treatment'. When there was no obvious 'no treatment' condition, then a comparison group was also selected using a random-selection procedure. Using this method, the programmes included in the review were therapeutic communities (16), methadone programmes (16), drug testing programmes (11), heroin programmes (6), supervision and aftercare (6), other treatment programmes (6), drug courts (5), psycho-social approaches (5), and other criminal justice interventions (4). The majority of studies (40) were based on a comparison of one type of treatment with another type of treatment (e.g. heroin compared with methadone). Twenty-eight studies compared one type of treatment with no treatment. The remaining seven studies were based on a comparison of different intensities of the same type of treatment (e.g. intensive supervision compared with regular supervision).

In most cases, only one data source was used (either self report or official records). When both data sources were used, self-report measures were chosen over official records on the grounds that they had the potential to provide fuller and more recent evidence of offending. Overall, the majority of studies used self-report data (60) and the remainder (15) used only official records.

Table 1. Description of Eligible Studies

Author	Date	Location	Design	Treatment	Comparison	Data source
Anglin et al.	1989	USA	Quasi	Other CJS	No treatment	Self report
Azrin et al.	1994	USA	Quasi	Psycho-Social	Other Treatment	Self report
Bale et al.	1980	USA	Random	Methadone	No Treatment	Self report
Beidler	1991	USA	Random	Other Treatment	Other Treatment	Self report
Bell	1997	AUST	Quasi	Methadone	Methadone	Self report
Brecht et al.	2006	USA	Quasi	Other CJS	No Treatment	Self-report
Brecht et al.	1993	USA	Quasi	TC	Other Treatment	Self Report
Britt et al.	1992	USA	Random	Drug Testing	No Treatment	Records
Brown et al.	2001	USA	Random	Supervision	No Treatment	Self report
Coviello et al	2001	USA	Quasi	Psycho-Social	Psycho-Social	Self report
Daley et al.	2000	USA	Quasi	TC	No Treatment	Self report
Deschenes et al.	1995	USA	Random	Supervision	No Treatment	Self report
Digiusto et al.	2006	AUST	Random	Methadone	Other Treatment	Self-report
Dijkgraaf et al.	2005	UK	Random	Heroin	Methadone	Self-report
Dynia & Sung	2000	USA	Quasi	TC	No Treatment	Records
Farabee et al.	2001	USA	Quasi	Supervision	No Treatment	Self report
Farrell	2000	USA	Random	TC	Other Treatment	Self report
French & Zarkin	1992	USA	Quasi	TC	Other Treatment	Self report
Ghodse et al.	2002	UK	Quasi	Supervision	Supervision	Self report
Gordon et al.	2000	USA	Random	TC	No Treatment	Records
Gossop et al.	2005	UK	Quasi	Methadone	TC	Records
Gossop et al.	2003	UK	Quasi	TC	Other Treatment	Self report
Gottfredson et al.	2007	USA	Random	Drug Court	No Treatment	Self-report
Gottfredson et al.	2003	USA	Random	Drug Court	No Treatment	Records
Graham-Bafus et al.	1984	USA	Quasi	Methadone	Other Treatment	Self report
Gunne & Grönbladh	1981	SWE	Random	Methadone	No Treatment	Self report
Haapanen & Britton	2002	USA	Random	Drug Testing	No Treatment	Records
Harris et al.	2005	UK	Random	Other Treatment	Methadone	Self-report
Hennggeler	1991	USA	Random	Psycho-Social	Other Treatment	Self report
Hoffmann & Miller	1992	USA	Quasi	Other Treatment	Other Treatment	Self report
Hough et al.	2003	UK	Quasi	Drug Testing	Other CJS	Records
Hser et al.	2001	USA	Quasi	TC	Other Treatment	Self report
Hubbard et al.	1997	USA	Quasi	Methadone	TC	Self report
Hubbard et al.	1989	USA	Quasi	TC	Other Treatment	Self report
Hughey & Klemke	1996	USA	Quasi	Other Treatment	No Treatment	Self report
Hutchinson et al.	2000	UK	Quasi	Methadone	Methadone	Self report
Inciardi et al.	1997	USA	Random	TC	Other Treatment	Self report

Author	Date	Location	Design	Treatment	Comparison	Data source
Jason et al.	2007	UK	Quasi	TC	Other Treatment	Self-report
Jones & Goldkamp	1993	USA	Random	Drug Testing	No Treatment	Self report
Kinlock et al.	2008	USA	Random	Methadone	Psycho-Social	Self-report
Knight et al.	1997	USA	Quasi	TC	Other CJS	Self-report
Kosten & Rounsaville	1987	USA	Quasi	Methadone	Other Treatment	Self report
Krebs et al.	2007	USA	Quasi	Drug Court	No Treatment	Records
Lam et al.	1995	USA	Quasi	Other Treatment	No Treatment	Self report
Latessa & Moon	1992	USA	Random	Other Treatment	No Treatment	Records
Magura	1993	USA	Quasi	Methadone	Other Treatment	Self report
March et al.	2006	USA	Quasi	Heroin	Methadone	Self-report
Marlowe et al.	2005	USA	Quasi	Drug Court	Drug Court	Self-report
Martin & Scarpitti	1993	USA	Random	Supervision	No Treatment	Self report
McBride & Inciardi	1993	USA	Random	Drug Testing	Other CJS	Self report
McCusker & Davies	1996	UK	Quasi	Heroin	Methadone	Self report
McGlothlin & Anglin	1981	USA	Quasi	Methadone	Methadone	Self report
McIvor	2004	SCOT	Quasi	Drug Testing	Drug Testing	Records
McLellan	1993	USA	Quasi	Psycho-Social	No Treatment	Self report
McSweeney et al.	2007	UK	Quasi	Other CJS	Other CJS	Self-report
Messina	1999	USA	Quasi	TC	TC	Self report
Metrebian et al.	2001	UK	Quasi	Heroin	Methadone	Self report
Mitchell & Herrell	2006	USA	Quasi	Drug Testing	No Treatment	Self-report
Naem et al.	2007	UK	Quasi	Drug Testing	Other Treatment	Self-report
Nemes et al.	1999	USA	Random	TC	TC	Records
Payne	2008	AUST	Quasi	Drug Testing	No Treatment	Records
Perneger et al.	1998	SWIT	Quasi	Heroin	Other Treatment	Self report
Robertson et al.	2006	UK	Random	Heroin	Methadone	Self-report
Schwartz	2007	UK	Quasi	Methadone	No Treatment	Self-report
Simpson & Sells	1982	USA	Quasi	Methadone	No Treatment	Self report
Simpson et al.	1997	USA	Quasi	TC	Other Treatment	Self report
Spohn et al.	2001	USA	Quasi	Drug Courts	No Treatment	Records
Strang et al.	2000	UK	Quasi	Methadone	Methadone	Self report
Taxman & Thanner	2006	USA	Random	Drug Testing	Other Treatment	Self-report
Teesson et al.	2006	AUST	Quasi	Methadone	No Treatment	Self-report
Turner et al.	1999	USA	Random	Drug Testing	Drug Court	Self report
Turner et al.	1992	USA	Random	Supervision	Supervision	Records
Wexler et al.	1999	USA	Random	TC	Other CJS	Records
Woody	1987	USA	Quasi	Psycho-Social	Other Treatment	Self report
Zhang	2001	USA	Quasi	Other CJS	No Treatment	Self report

IV. Results

Two methods were used to summarise the results of the selected studies. The first is a *narrative review,* which presents descriptive summaries of the results obtained. The findings are presented in the form of relative percentage change in crime among the experimental group compared with the control group over time in the case of quasi-experimental designs and the difference in outcome measures following treatment in the case of post-test only random allocation designs. The second method is a *meta-analysis,* which involves recalculating the published findings to produce a standardised effect size for each study.

Narrative Review

The first method is referred to as a quantitative narrative review. The analysis is quantitative in as much as numerical results presented in the study are summarised. The analysis is narrative in as much as the results are presented mainly in a descriptive form. In some cases, when percentages are not reported in the publication, the authors' verbatim conclusions are used. The main benefit of including a quantitative review in addition to a meta analysis is that it is possible to include more studies in the review. A meta analysis requires extraction of raw data, which is only possible from the most detailed publications.

The results of the quantitative part of the narrative review are shown in Table 2. The table provides details of all 75 studies used in the review, including the type of treatment being evaluated, the research design, the relative percentage change over time in experimental and comparison groups (in the case of quasi-experimental studies), and the mean percentage difference between experimental and comparison groups in the post-test period (in the case of random allocation studies). The final column shows the outcome of the study as determined by the methods described above. A positive outcome means that the experimental group performed better than the comparison group in terms of subsequent criminal behaviour. A negative result means that the experimental group did less well than the comparison group and an equal result means that the outcome for both groups was the same.

Table 2. Narrative Review Results on the Effectiveness of Treatment on Offending

Percentages

Author	Treatment	Design	Experimental	Comparison	Outcome
Gottfredson et al.	Drug Court	Random	66	81	Positive
Gottfredson et al.	Drug Court	Random	0.05 (mean)	0.09 (mean)	Positive
Krebs et al.	Drug Court	Quasi	no numerical data	no numerical data	Positive
Marlowe et al.	Drug Court	Quasi	-25	-59	Negative
Spohn et al.	Drug Court	Quasi	+10	+29	Positive
Britt et al.	Drug Testing	Random	25	24	Negative
Haapanen and Britton	Drug Testing	Random	33	27	Negative
Hough et al.	Drug Testing	Quasi	+80	+91	Positive
Jones and Goldkamp	Drug Testing	Random	10	12	Positive
McBride and Inciardi	Drug Testing	Random	5	4	Negative
McIvor	Drug Testing	Quasi	-48	-29	Positive
Mitchell and Herrell	Drug Testing	Quasi	-64	+92	Positive
Naeem et al.	Drug Testing	Quasi	-33	-18	Positive
Payne	Drug Testing	Quasi	-86	-61	Positive
Taxman and Thanner	Drug Testing	Random	56	57	Positive
Turner et al.	Drug Testing	Random	15	10	Negative
Dijkgraaf et al.	Heroin	Random	25 (mean)	54 (mean)	Positive
March et al.	Heroin	Quasi	-95	-49	Positive
McCusker and Davies	Heroin	Quasi	-13	-28	Negative
Metrebian et al.	Heroin	Quasi	-95	-53	Positive
Perneger et al.	Heroin	Quasi	-86	+150	Positive
Robertson et al.	Heroin	Random	51	51	Equal
Bale et al.	Methadone	Random	49	54	Positive
Bell	Methadone	Quasi	-44	-75	Negative
Digiusto et al.	Methadone	Random	9	9	Equal
Gossop et al.	Methadone	Quasi	-72	-73	Negative
Graham-Bafus et al.	Methadone	Quasi	no numerical data	no numerical data	Equal
Gunne and Grönbladh	Methadone	Random	6	13	Positive
Hubbard et al.	Methadone	Quasi	-71	-88	Negative
Hutchinson et al.	Methadone	Quasi	-75	-30	Positive
Kinlock et al.	Methadone	Random	29	56	Positive

Author	Treatment	Design	Experimental	Comparison	Outcome
Kosten and Rounsaville	Methadone	Quasi	-81	-84	Negative
Magura	Methadone	Quasi	-23	-19	Positive
McGlothlin and Anglin	Methadone	Quasi	-75	-30	Positive
Schwartz	Methadone	Quasi	-95	-56	Positive
Simpson and Sells	Methadone	Quasi	-69	-55	Positive
Strang et al.	Methadone	Quasi	-69	-36	Positive
Teesson et al.	Methadone	Quasi	-58	-34	Positive
Anglin et al.	Other CJS	Quasi	-50	-50	Equal
Brecht et al.	Other CJS	Quasi	-63	-67	Negative
McSweeney et al.	Other CJS	Quasi	-71	-69	Positive
Zhang	Other CJS	Quasi	-79	-85	Negative
Beidler	Other Treatment	Random	n/a	n/a	Equal
Harris et al.	Other Treatment	Random	5	9	Positive
Hoffmann and Miller	Other Treatment	Quasi	-56	-64	Negative
Hughey and Klemke	Other Treatment	Quasi	-52	-54	Negative
Lam et al.	Other Treatment	Quasi	-61	-49	Positive
Latessa and Moon	Other Treatment	Random	20	18	Negative
Azrin et al.	Psycho-Social	Quasi	-77	-69	Positive
Coviello et al	Psycho-Social	Quasi	-33	+25	Positive
Hennggeler	Psycho-Social	Random	4	16	Positive
McLellan	Psycho-Social	Quasi	-67	0	Positive
Woody	Psycho-Social	Quasi	-40	+100	Positive
Brown et al.	Supervision	Random	19	16	Negative
Deschenes et al.	Supervision	Random	15	21	Positive
Farabee et al.	Supervision	Quasi	-67	-23	Positive
Ghoodse et al.	Supervision	Quasi	-75	-25	Positive
Martin and Scarpitti	Supervision	Random	46	51	Positive
Turner et al.	Supervision	Random	13	10	Negative
Brecht et al.	TC	Quasi	-60	-47	Positive
Daley et al.	TC	Quasi	-88	-74	Positive
Dynia and Sung	TC	Quasi	-71	-44	Positive
Farrell	TC	Random	39	39	Equal
French and Zarkin	TC	Quasi	-54	-23	Positive

Author	Treatment	Design	Experimental	Comparison	Outcome
Gordon et al.	TC	Random	31	44	Positive
Gossop et al.	TC	Quasi	-49	-45	Positive
Hser et al.	TC	Quasi	-52	-18	Positive
Hubbard et al.	TC	Quasi	-67	-77	Negative
Inciardi et al.	TC	Random	23	54	Positive
Jason et al.	TC	Quasi	-100	-60	Positive
Knight et al.	TC	Quasi	n/a	n/a	Positive
Messina	TC	Quasi	n/a	n/a	Positive
Nemes et al.	TC	Random	17	26	Positive
Simpson et al.	TC	Quasi	-40	-32	Positive
Wexler et al.	TC	Random	8	50	Positive

Note: All numbers are percentages with the exception of two means which are marked in the table in parentheses.

Table 3. Summary of the Narrative Review Results on the Effectiveness of Treatment on Offending

Treatment	Outcome (% positive)
Psycho-Social	100% (n=5)
Therapeutic communities	88% (n=16)
Drug Court	80% (n=5)
Heroin treatment	67% (n=6)
Supervision	67% (n=6)
Drug Testing	64% (n=11)
Methadone treatment	63% (n=16)
Other treatment programmes	33% (n=6)
Other CJS programmes	25% (n=4)
Total	68% (n=75)

A summary of the results of the review is shown in Table 3. Overall, 68 per cent of the outcomes were classified as positive (the treatment group performed better than the comparison group in terms of subsequent criminal behaviour). In other words, the results of the narrative review show that in the majority of cases treatment worked in terms of subsequent criminal behaviour.

It is possible that some treatment programmes work better than others. The table shows that in seven of the nine treatment types the majority of studies produced positive findings. It was only in relation to other treatment programmes and other criminal justice system programmes that the percentage of positive outcomes fell below 50 per cent. The most successful programmes involved some kind of therapeutic method. Short summaries of selected examples of evaluations of each of the programme types are listed below.

Psycho-social approaches

WOODY ET AL. (1987) evaluated the effectiveness of psychotherapy among 93 male veterans who were addicted to opiates and were receiving methadone maintenance treatment. The subjects were randomly assigned to one of three conditions: (1) drug counselling alone, (2) counselling plus supportive-expressive psychotherapy, or (3) counselling plus cognitive-behavioural psychotherapy. Interviews were conducted with the subjects at intake and 12 months later. Among the supportive-expressive psychotherapy group, the mean number of days spent committing crimes decreased from 5 at baseline to 3 at 12-month follow-up. By contrast, among the drug counselling alone group the mean number of days spent committing crimes increased from 2 to 4. The authors concluded that "the two psychotherapy groups showed more improvements than the drug counselling group over a wider range of outcome measures, with marked changes in the areas of employment, legal status, and psychiatric symptoms and with less use of psychotropic medications" (p.595).

Therapeutic communities

WEXLER ET AL. (1999) evaluated the effectiveness of an in-prison therapeutic community in the USA. Seven hundred and fifteen inmates were randomly assigned to either the prison therapeutic community group or to a no-treatment control group. The results showed a greater reduction in criminal behaviour among prisoners offered therapeutic community treatment than those on the normal prison routine. At 24-month follow-up, 14 per cent of subjects who had completed therapeutic community treatment and aftercare had been reincarcerated, compared with 67 per cent of subjects in the no-treatment group. The authors claimed that their findings "support the efficacy of prison TC plus aftercare in reducing reincarceration rates among inmates treated for substance abuse." (p.147)

Drug courts

TURNER ET AL. (1999) compared the efficacy of drug courts with the efficacy of drug testing. Five hundred and six subjects were randomly allocated into either the drug testing group or the drug court group. At 36-month follow-up, a smaller proportion of subjects in the drug court group than in the drug testing group were arrested for any offence (33% compared with 44%) and for property offences (10% compared with 15%). The drug court group was also associated with a smaller mean number of arrests (0.6 compared with 0.8).

Heroin treatment

METREBIAN ET AL. (2001) conducted a study that compared the efficacy of injectable heroin and injectable methadone in the treatment of opiate dependent drug users. A sample of 58 drug users, recruited from a West London drug clinic, was given the choice of receiving injectable heroin or injectable methadone. Thirty-seven subjects chose heroin and 21 chose methadone. Interviews were conducted with the two groups of subjects at entry into treatment and 12 months later. At 12-month follow-up, the criminal activity score among subjects who received injectable heroin had decreased significantly from 1.9 to 0.1 (a 95% reduction). The criminal activity score among subjects who received injectable methadone decreased from 1.9 to 0.9 (a 53% reduction). The authors explain that "While those choosing each drug had different baseline characteristics, both groups were well retained in treatment and at 3 months made significant reductions in drug use and crime, which were well sustained over the 12-month follow-up period." (p.267)

Supervision

GHODSE ET AL. (2002) conducted a study in the UK that explored the impact of aftercare among 49 patients who had undergone residential opiate detoxification. The comparison group received detoxification without aftercare. The results indicated that detoxification plus aftercare was more effective than detoxification without aftercare in reducing criminal behaviour. Among subjects in the aftercare group, the mean number of drug-related crime days reduced from 59 days in the three months before treatment to six days in the three month follow-up period (a 90% decrease). Among subjects in the no aftercare group, the mean number of drug-related crime days reduced from 44 days to 19 days (a 57% decrease). The authors conclude that "Significantly better treatment outcome was observed amongst those who completed detoxification and went on to spend at least 6 weeks in recovery and/or residential rehabilitation unit." (p.776)

Drug Testing

HAAPANEN AND BRITTON (2002) conducted an experimental study that examined the parole outcomes and arrests for 1,958 parolees in the USA. Subjects were randomly assigned to various levels of routine drug testing ranging from no-testing to two tests per month. The results showed that frequent drug testing was less effective than no-testing in reducing criminal behaviour. At 42-month follow-up, the mean number of arrests for the drug testing group was 3.8 compared to 3.0 for the no-testing group. The mean arrest rates for property crimes and drug crimes were also lower among the no-testing group than the testing group.

Methadone treatment

MAGURA ET AL. (1993) investigated the effectiveness of an in-prison methadone maintenance programme in the USA in reducing subsequent criminal behaviour. Subjects receiving methadone maintenance were compared with similar subjects who received seven-day heroin detoxification. Criminal behaviour was assessed in the six months before intake and six months after treatment. The mean number of offences committed in the post-release period decreased from 117 to 66 offences (a 44% decrease) among the methadone group and from 65 to 49 offences (a 25% decrease) among the detoxification group. There was also a decrease in the number of subjects reporting illegal income in the last seven days among both groups (23% for the methadone group and 19% for the detoxification group).

Other treatment programmes

LATESSA AND MOON (1992) examined the effectiveness of acupuncture in an outpatient drug treatment programme. A sample of 274 chemically dependent offenders in the USA was randomly allocated into one of three groups: an experimental group that received acupuncture on a regular basis, a control group that did not receive any form of acupuncture, and a placebo group that received an acupuncture-like simulation. Using official records, the authors compared the groups in terms of new arrests, convictions and technical violations incurred over the evaluation period (120-160 days). The figures showed that a smaller proportion of subjects in the control group than in the acupuncture group were convicted or arrested for a felony offence over the study period. There was little difference between the two groups in terms of the proportions with any conviction (15% of the acupuncture group and 16% of the control group). The authors concluded that "there is no evidence that acupuncture had any appreciable effect on programme completion, arrests, convictions, or probation outcome." (p.330)

Other criminal justice system programmes

BRECHT ET AL. (1993) investigated the impact of legal coercion on treatment effectiveness among a sample of 618 methadone maintenance clients. Subjects were recruited from treatment programmes in the USA and were divided into three groups on the basis of the level of legal coercion that they were under (high, moderate or low). In the high coercion group subjects reported a mean of three burglary days a month in the pre-treatment period and one burglary day a month in the post treatment period (a 67% reduction). In the low coercion group, the mean burglary days decreased from one to zero from the pre to post treatment period. The authors note that "those coerced into treatment respond in ways similar to voluntary admissions regardless of gender or ethnicity." (p.89)

Meta Analysis

The main aim of the meta analysis is to generate a standardised measure of effectiveness that is comparable across studies. In so doing, individual studies can be compared directly using the same outcome measure. The meta analysis also enables average outcomes to be calculated for all studies or specific groups of studies.

In order to carry out the meta analysis, a comparable effect size measure is needed for each evaluation (see Lipsey and Wilson, 2001). The effect size used in the current review is the Odds Ratio (OR). In order to calculate the OR, sufficient information must be presented in the published study report. In just under half of studies (n=37) included in the narrative review (n=75) an OR could be calculated from the published data.

The crime outcome measures used in the analysis included both criminal justice measures (re-arrests, reconvictions, and re-imprisonment) and crime measures (reported crime, property crime, illegal income, and thefts). There were no studies in the review that provided sufficient information (e.g. standard deviations) to allow ORs to be calculated from mean offending rates. Hence, the meta analysis is based on ORs derived solely from frequencies or proportions.

Individual effect sizes

The ORs for the 37 individual studies used in the meta analysis are shown numerically in Table 4 and graphically in Figure 1.

Table 4. Meta Analysis Results on the Effectiveness of Treatment on Offending
n=37

Author	Date	Outcome measure	Treatment type	OR	CI lower	CI upper	p
Bale et al.	1980	% arrested	Methadone	1.24	0.70	2.20	ns
Britt et al.	1992	% arrested	Drug Testing	0.93	0.52	1.69	ns
Brown et al.	2001	% any crime	Supervision	0.82	0.31	2.19	ns
Deschenes et al.	1995	% arrested	Supervision	1.54	0.70	3.35	ns
Digiusto et al.	2006	% property crime	Methadone	0.95	0.39	2.32	ns
Dynia and Sung	2000	% arrested	TC	2.16	1.10	4.23	Significant
Farabee et al.	2001	% arrested	Supervision	3.10	1.80	5.34	Significant
Farrell	2000	% recidivating	TC	1.02	0.41	2.52	ns
Ghoodse et al.	2002	% offended	Supervision	13.13	1.59	108.32	Significant

Author	Date	Outcome measure	Treatment type	OR	CI lower	CI upper	p
Gordon et al.	2000	% reconvicted	TC	1.70	1.17	2.48	Significant
Gossop et al.	2003	% convictions	TC	0.99	0.64	1.52	ns
Gottfredson et al.	2003	% rearrested	Drug Court	2.21	1.19	4.12	Significant
Haapanen and Britton	2002	% rearrested property	Drug Testing	0.74	0.51	1.09	ns
Harris et al.	2005	% property crime	Other Treatment	1.85	0.29	11.80	ns
Hoffmann and Miller	1992	% arrested	Other Treatment	0.80	0.53	1.20	ns
Hser et al.	2001	% arrested	TC	3.77	2.53	5.62	Significant
Hubbard et al.	1997	% predatory crime	Methadone	0.69	0.50	0.97	ns
Hutchinson et al.	2000	% drug offences	Methadone	3.07	0.45	20.82	ns
Inciardi et al.	1997	% arrest-free	TC	3.86	1.79	8.29	Significant
Jason et al.	2007	% with charges	TC	4.91	0.44	54.27	ns
Kinlock et al.	2008	% criminal activity	Methadone	3.21	1.54	6.67	Significant
Latessa and Moon	1992	% arrested	Other Treatment	0.88	0.38	2.06	ns
Magura	1993	% illegal income	Methadone	1.57	0.57	4.29	ns
Marlowe et al.	2005	% criminal activity	Drug Court	0.47	0.16	1.40	ns
Martin and Scarpitti	1993	% re-imprisoned	Supervision	1.19	0.58	2.45	ns
McBride and Inciardi	1993	% rearrested	Drug Testing	0.92	0.58	1.47	ns
McIvor	2004	% convicted	Drug Testing	1.43	0.64	3.22	ns
Nemes et al.	1999	% arrested	TC	1.73	1.07	2.79	Significant
Perneger et al.	1998	% property/ theft	Heroin	27.02	1.64	445.98	Significant
Robertson et al.	2006	% incarcerated	Heroin	0.99	0.59	1.70	ns
Simpson and Sells	1982	% arrested	Methadone	2.02	1.09	3.75	Significant
Simpson et al.	1997	% arrested	TC	1.44	0.83	2.51	ns

Author	Date	Outcome measure	Treatment type	OR	CI lower	CI upper	p
Strang et al.	2000	% acquisitive crimes	Methadone	2.90	0.34	24.94	ns
Taxman and Thanner	2006	% arrested	Drug Testing	1.06	0.49	2.26	ns
Teesson et al.	2006	% criminal activity	Methadone	1.50	0.62	3.65	ns
Turner et al.	1999	% arrested property	Drug Testing	0.61	0.33	1.13	ns
Wexler et al.	1999	% reincarcerated	TC	10.97	5.14	23.44	Significant

Table 4 shows that 25 of the 37 studies (68%) produced ORs greater than 1 showing a potential favourable effect on criminal behaviour and 12 of the 37 studies (32%) produced ORs below 1 showing a potential unfavourable effect. Hence, the majority of studies showed that treatment was followed by a desirable change in criminal behaviour (either a greater reduction or a smaller increase). However, ORs which have confidence intervals that include the value 1 are not statistically significant as their measured OR might have occurred by chance. In total, 12 of the 37 studies have confidence intervals that do not span the value 1 and can be considered statistically significant. All of these studies provide values of OR greater than 1. Hence, all 12 of the significant findings show that treatment is associated with a favourable outcome in terms of criminal behaviour. The results are shown graphically in Figure 1. ORs to the right of the chance value of 1 show a favourable outcome and those to the left of 1 show an unfavourable outcome. The majority of studies fall to the right of value 1 and 12 of these have error bars that do not span the value 1.

Figure1. Forest Plot of the Effectiveness of Treatment in Reducing Crime

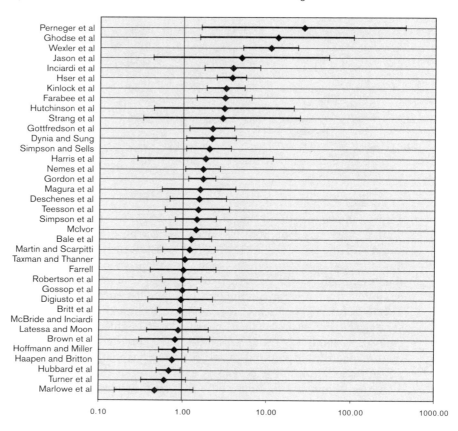

Notes: Odds ratios and confidence intervals shown on a logarithmic scale.

Mean effect sizes

The main aim of a meta-analysis is to calculate a weighted mean effect size (here, the OR) for all studies and for specific groups of studies. There are two ways of calculating the weighted mean effect size. In the fixed effects (FE) model, each effect size is weighted by the inverse of its variance (1/VAR), so that studies based on larger samples are given greater weighting. However, the studies in a fixed effects model can be significantly heterogeneous in their effect sizes (measured by the Q statistic). This can mean that a single study with a large effect size can disproportionately influence the average effect size. One method of addressing the problem of heterogeneity is to perform a 'random effects' meta analysis. The random effects (RE) model is designed primarily to minimize the heterogeneity of a set of effect sizes by adding a constant to the variance of each effect size (for the formula, see Lipsey & Wilson, 2001, p.119). In the random effects model, each study is given a more equal weighting in calculating the weighted mean effect size, so larger studies no longer have such a great influence on the mean.

In the following meta analyses, we have used the (FE) model only. The main advantages of this method are that it is more straight forward and transparent in its method of weighting the effect size (i.e. the inverse of its variance). The main disadvantages of the (FE) model are that the average effect size can be affected by variations among the studies in their effect size. Studies with extreme effect sizes and large n's can have a disproportionate effect on the average results. However, it is generally not possible to remove all variations among studies whatever method is used and on balance it is clearer to present the results of just one method rather than two.

The mean effect size for all studies combined was 1.35 (see Table 5). This was statistically significant (z = 5.83, p<.0001). This means that the odds of crime increased by 35 per cent among the comparison groups compared with the experimental groups or decreased by 26 per cent in the experimental groups compared with the comparison groups.

Moderator analyses

Overall, the meta analysis has shown that treatment is associated with favourable changes in crime. However, it is possible that this result might vary depending of various features of the programme, the client group, or the research design. In order to consider this, a moderator analysis was conducted to determine if there were any important differences in outcome depending on various features of the evaluation. The results are shown in Table 5 and 6.

The first variable considered was the effect of the treatment type on outcomes. Table 5 shows the mean ORs for seven of the nine treatment modalities investigated (the remaining two did not have any evaluations which matched our eligibility criteria for inclusion in the meta analysis). Five of the seven programmes were associated with mean ORs greater than 1 suggesting a favourable impact on crime and two with values less than 1 suggesting an unfavourable impact. However, ORs with confidence intervals that include 1 are not statistically significant and could have occurred by chance. Only two of the studies produced ORs that were statistically significant: therapeutic communities (OR=2.06) and supervision (OR=1.89). Hence, according to the meta-analysis, these were the only two treatment types associated with a statistically significant reduction in criminal behaviour. In the case of therapeutic communities, the OR of 2.06 represents an average reduction within the experimental group of over 50 per cent and in the case of supervision an average reduction of just under 50 per cent.

Table 5. Meta Analysis Results by Type of Treatment

Treatment	No. of studies	OR	CI lower	CI (upper)	Sig of diff. o
Therapeutic Communities	10	2.06	1.73	2.45	Significant
Supervision	5	1.89	1.34	2.69	Significant
Drug courts	2	1.52	0.88	2.60	ns
Methadone	9	1.14	0.92	1.42	ns
Heroin	2	1.12	0.66	1.89	ns
Drug Testing	6	0.85	0.68	1.06	ns
Other Treatment	3	0.84	0.58	1.20	ns
All studies	37	1.35	1.22	1.50	Significant

Table 6. Meta Analysis Results by Features of the Programme

Features of the programme	No. of studies	OR	CI (lower)	CI (upper)	Sig of diff. of ORs
Design					
Random	20	1.31	1.15	1.51	
Quasi	17	1.40	1.21	1.63	ns
Comparison [1]					
T1 v T0	16	1.60	1.37	1.86	
T1 v T2	15	1.14	0.99	1.32	Significant
Context					
Criminal justice	19	1.44	1.24	1.66	
Treatment	18	1.28	1.11	1.47	ns
Country					
US	27	1.38	1.24	1.54	
UK + other	10	1.21	0.92	1.58	ns
Year					
1980s + 1990s	16	1.17	1.02	1.36	
2000s	21	1.55	1.35	1.79	Significant
All studies	37	1.35	1.22	1.50	

Notes: [1] T1a v T1b (n=6) have been omitted from this analysis.

The effect of other features of the treatment or the research design is presented in Table 6. There is no evidence that the type of evaluation design was associated with the research outcomes. Quasi experimental designs had a slightly higher OR (1.40) than random designs (1.31), but the difference between the two ORs was not statistically significant.

It is also possible that the type of comparison might influence outcomes. Evaluations were typically based on comparing treatment with no treatment or an alternative treatment. It might be expected that comparisons based on treatment and no treatment would be more likely to identify a difference in outcome than comparisons based on one form of treatment with another form. The results supported this assumption showing that treatment versus no treatment evaluations produced higher ORs than those that compared one treatment with another. In other words, it appears harder to show a positive programme effect when two treatments are being compared.

The third moderator considered is whether the context of the treatment is important. A comparison was made between programmes that were implemented within the context of the criminal justice system and programmes outside of this context. The results showed that there was no significant difference in the effect sizes of treatment programmes based on standard referral compared with programmes based on criminal justice referral processes.

It is also possible that treatment implemented in one country might have different outcomes than treatment implemented in another country. A comparison of the effectiveness of treatment implemented in the USA and treatment implemented in the UK and other countries showed no significant difference between the two.

Finally, a comparison was made between treatment programmes that were implemented and evaluated before the year 2000 and those implemented from 2000 and after. It might be the case that treatment of drug use has become more effective over time as a result of enhanced procedures or general experience in dealing with drug users. The results provided some support for this proposition by showing a significantly greater effect on criminal behaviour among more recent treatment programmes than earlier programmes.

V. Conclusion

The results of previous systematic reviews of the effectiveness of drug treatment programmes are far from conclusive. Marsch (1998) found that methadone treatment programmes were associated with reduced rates of offending while Mitchell et al (2005) found that it resulted in higher rates. Similarly, one of the two reviews that included group counselling (Mitchell et al. 2005) found that it was effective in reducing crime whilst the other (Pearson and Lipton, 1998) reported that it was not effective. With regard to therapeutic communities, three reviews concluded that they were effective in reducing offending, although one found that it was no more effective than other drug treatment methods. The one review that examined the effectiveness of naltrexone maintenance treatment in preventing crime (Kirchmayer et al. 2002) found that it was effective in reducing re-incarceration.

The main finding of the *narrative review* was that in over two-thirds of studies the treatment group performed better than the comparison group in terms of subsequent criminal behaviour. In other words, in the majority of cases, treatment was associated with a reduction in crime. However, some treatment programmes were found to work better than others. The most successful programmes involved some kind of psycho-social therapeutic method. The main finding of the *meta-analysis* was that treatment programmes were generally associated with a relative reduction in crime of about 26 per cent. Therapeutic communities and supervision programmes were associated with the largest reductions in crime (51% and 47% respectively). The positive findings of the narrative review are consistent with the positive effect found in the meta-analysis. Hence, the dominant finding of this review, using both methods, is that treatment programmes (especially psycho-social therapeutic programmes) are effective in reducing criminal behaviour.

It is difficult to explain the difference in effectiveness of programmes on criminal behaviour. The programmes involved are quite different in terms of the methods adopted and the mechanisms by which these methods might become converted into behavioural changes are rarely discussed. It is possible that some of the difference might relate to the quality and intensity of the programme. Methadone maintenance programmes, for example, may last for many months or even years. Conversely, some drug testing programmes (e.g. simple monitoring) may last just for the time it takes to administer the test.

Implications for research

There are a number of implications for future evaluation research on the effectiveness of drug treatment on criminal behaviour.

First, most of the studies selected were conducted in the USA and the remainder were restricted to the UK and a few other countries.

This geographical pattern might reflect the fact that only those studies written in the English language were eligible for inclusion in the review. However, bibliographic databases (such as IBSS), include translated English titles for papers written in other languages. Hence, the lack of studies from countries other than the US and the UK is more likely to be a reflection of the limited amount of evaluation research conducted in these countries rather than a reflection of the language selection criteria.

Second, there are problems with the quality of research evaluations. The majority of studies originally selected were eventually excluded on the grounds that they did not meet the minimum standards of methodological quality. It is important that evaluative research is based on sufficiently sound research methods to allow interpretable findings.

Third, there was a strong reliance among evaluations on quasi-experimental designs rather than randomised controlled trials. It is possible that quasi-experimental designs are prone to selection bias whereby the most promising clients are allocated to the experimental treatment. It would improve the overall quality of evaluations if they were based on random allocation designs.

Fourth, the results of evaluations can be affected by the type of comparison group used. Treatment versus no treatment comparisons provide the strongest and most encouraging results. However, many evaluations are based on comparisons of treatment versus other treatment. These can underestimate the effectiveness of a programme as the comparison intervention might also be effective. Hence, future research should try to use comparison groups that do not receive treatment.

Finally, many studies were excluded from the meta-analysis because the results were not presented in a way that would allow an effect size to be calculated. It would be helpful if published evaluations included raw data, cell sizes and other relevant information in order to facilitate future meta-analyses.

Implications for policy

The first implication for policy is that there is some evidence from this review that drug treatment can be effective in reducing crime. This provides support for existing policy and strengthens the evidence base for future policies. However, it must also be recognised that there is some variation in effectiveness across studies and it is still generally unclear how drug treatment leads to a reduction in criminal behaviour.

The second policy implication is the finding that some programmes work better than others. Government drugs policies tend not to be specific about the type of treatment that should be used to reduce drug-related crime. However, the current review suggests that some programmes such as therapeutic communities, psycho-social approaches, and supervision are more effective in reducing criminal behaviour than alternative treatments. It might be beneficial for policy to prioritise the use of those treatment programmes that have the best chances of success.

Finally, the link between policy and evaluative research might be better integrated and strengthened. This might involve a funded programme of research that could co-ordinate evaluations in terms of treatment methods investigated and research designs. Governments might also issue guidelines on good practice in conducting evaluative research to ensure that the results were comparable across studies and locations. Overall, governments should become more directly involved in the process of generating an empirical base for evidence-based drugs policy.

References

Previous Reviews of the Literature

Chanhatasilpa, C., MacKenzie, D. and Hickman, L. (2000) 'The effectiveness of community-based programmes for chemically dependent offenders: A review and assessment of the research', *Journal of Substance Abuse Treatment*, 19, 383-393.

Hall, W. (1996) 'Methadone maintenance treatment as a crime control measure', *Crime and Justice Bulletin, 29*, New South Wales Bureau of Crime and Statistics and Research.

Kirchmayer, U., Davoli, M., Verster, D., Amato, L., Ferri, M. and Peruccia, C.A. (2002) 'A systematic review on the efficacy of naltrexone maintenance treatment in opioid dependence', *Addiction*, 97, 1241-1249.

Marsch, L. (1998) 'The efficacy of methadone maintenance interventions in reducing illicit opiate use, HIV risk behaviour and criminality: a meta-analysis', *Addiction*, 93(4), 515-532.

Mitchell, O., MacKenzie, D.L. and Wilson, D.B. (2006) 'Incarceration-based drug treatment', in B.C. Welsh and D.P. Farrington (Eds.): *Preventing Crime: What Works for Children, Offenders, Victims and Places* (103-116), Dordrecht, Netherlands: Springer.

Pearson, F. and Lipton, D. (1999) 'A meta-analytic review of the effectiveness of corrections-based treatments for drug abuse', *Prison Journal*, 79 (4), 384-410.

Prendergast, M., Podus, D., Chang, E., and Urada, D. (2002) 'The effectiveness of drug abuse treatment: a meta-analysis of comparison group studies', *Drug and Alcohol Dependence*, 67(1), 53-72.

Vaughn, M.G. and Howard, M.O. (2004) 'Adolescent substance abuse treatment: a synthesis of controlled evaluations', *Research on Social Work Practice*, 14, 325-335.

Wilson, David B., Mitchell, O., and MacKenzie, D.L. (2006) A systematic review of drug court effects on recidivism. *Journal of Experimental Criminology*, 2(4): 459-487.

Included Studies

Anglin, D., Brecht, M., and Maddahain, E. (1989) 'Pretreatment characteristics and treatment performance of legally coerced versus voluntary methadone maintenance admissions', *Criminology*, 27(3), 537-557.

Azrin, N., McMahon, P., Donohue, B., Besalel, V., Lapinski, K., Kogan, E., Acierno, R., and Galloway, E. (1994) 'Behaviour therapy for drug abuse: a controlled treatment outcome study', *Behavioural Research Therapy*, 32(8), 857-866.

Bale, R.N., Van Stone, W.W., Kuldau, J.M., Engelsing, T.M.J., Elashoff, R.M., and Zarcone, V.P. (1980) 'Therapeutic communities vs methadone maintenance', *Archives of General Psychiatry*, 37, 179-193.

Beidler, R.J. (1991) 'Treating drug addicts and alcoholics together: a clinical trial', *Journal of Addictive Diseases*, 10(3), pp 81-96.

Bell, J. (1997) 'Methadone maintenance and property crime', Paper presented at the Second National Outlook Symposium on Crime, Canberra, Australia (March 3-4).

Brecht, M.L., Anglin, M.D., and Wang, J.C. (1993) 'Treatment effectiveness for legally coerced versus voluntary methadone maintenance clients', *American Journal of Drug and Alcohol Abuse*, 19(1), 89-106.

Brecht, M.L., Greenwell, L., von Mayrhauser, C. and Anglin, M.D. (2006) 'Two-year outcomes of treatment for methamphetamine use', *Journal of Psychoactive Drugs*, SARC Supplement 3, 415-426.

Britt, C.L., Gottfredson, M.R., and Goldkamp, J.S. (1992) 'Drug testing and pretrial misconduct: an experiment on the specific deterrent effects of drug monitoring dependents on pretrial release', *Journal of Research in Crime and Delinquency*, 29(1), 62-78.

Brown, B.S., O'Grady, K.E., Battjes, R.J., Farrell, E.V., Smith, N.P., and Nurco, D.N. (2001), 'Effectiveness of a stand-alone aftercare programme for drug-involved offenders', *Journal of Substance Abuse Treatment*, 21, 185-192.

Coviello, D., Alterman, A., Rutherford, M., Cacciola, J., McKay, J., and Zanis, D. (2001) 'The effectiveness of two intensities of psychosocial treatment for cocaine dependence', *Drug and Alcohol Dependence, 61,* 145-154.

Daley, M., Argeriou, M., McCarty, D., Callahan, J.J., Shepard, D.S., and Williams, C.N. (2000) 'The costs of crime and the benefits of substance abuse treatment for pregnant women', *Journal of Substance Abuse Treatment*, 19, 445-458.

Deschenes, E.P., Turner, S., and Petersilia, J. (1995) 'A dual experiment in intensive community supervision: Minnesota's prison diversion and enhanced supervised release programmes', *The Prison Journal*, 75(3), 330-356.

Digiusto, E., Shakeshaft, A. P., Ritter, A. (2006) 'Effects of pharmacotherapies for opioid dependence on participants criminal behaviour and expenditure on illicit drugs: An Australian National Evaluation (NEPOD)', *Australian and New Zealand Journal of Criminology*, 39(2), 171-189.

Dijkgraaf, M.G.W., van der Zanden B.P., de Borgie, C.A.J.M., Blanken, P., Van Ree, J.M., and van den Brink, W. (2005) 'Cost utility analysis of co-prescribed heroin compared with methadone maintenance treatment in heroin addicts in two randomised trials', *British Medical Journal*, 330, 1297-1300.

Dynia, P. and Sung, H. (2000), 'The safety and effectiveness of diverting felony drug offenders to residential treatment as measured by recidivism', *Criminal Justice Policy Review*, 11(4), 299-311.

Farabee, D., Shen, H., Hser, Y., Grella, C., and Anglin, M. (2001). 'The effect of drug treatment on criminal behaviour among adolescents in DATOS-A, *Journal of Adolescent Research*, 16 (6), 679-696.

Farrell, A. (2000). 'Women, crime and drugs: testing the effect of therapeutic communities', *Women and Criminal Justice*, 11(1), 21-48.

French, M., Zarkin, G. (1992) 'Effects of drug abuse treatment on legal and illegal earnings', *Contemporary Policy Issues*, 10(2), 98-110.

Ghodse, H., Reynolds, M., Baldacchino, A., Dunmore, E., Byrne, S., Oyefeso, A., Clancy, C., and Crawford, V. (2002) 'Treating an opiate-dependent inpatient population: A one-year follow-up study of treatment completers and noncompleters', *Addictive Behaviours*, 27, 765-778.

Gordon, J., Moriarty, L. and Grant, P. (2000) 'The Impact of a Juvenile Residential Treatment Center on Minority Offenders', *Journal of Criminal Justice*, 16(2), 194-208.

Gossop, M., Marsden, J., Stewart, D., and Kidd, T. (2003) 'The national treatment outcome research study (NTORS): 4-5 year follow-up results', *Addiction*, 98, 291-303.

Gossop, M., Trakada, K., Stewart, D. (2005) 'Reductions in criminal convictions after addiction treatment: 5 year follow-up', *Drug and Alcohol Dependence*, 79(3), 295-302.

Gottfredson, D. and Exum, M. (2002) 'The Baltimore City Drug Treatment Court: One-year results from a randomized study', *Journal of Research in Crime and Delinquency*, 39(3), 337-356.

Gottfredson, D. C., Kearley, B. W., Najaka, S. S., Rocha, C. M. (2007) 'How Drug Treatment Courts Work: An Analysis of Mediators', *Journal of Research in Crime and Delinquency*, 44(1), 3-35.

Gottfredson, D.C., Najaka, S.S., and Kearley, B. (2003) 'Effectiveness of drug treatment courts: evidence from a randomized trial', *Criminology and Public Policy, 2(2)*, 171-196.

Graham-Bafus, S., Allen, R.H., Gordon, J.R. (1984), 'Evaluation of a methadone rehabilitation program', *Psychological Reports*, 55, 99-106.

Gunne, L-M. and Grönbladh, L. (1981), 'The Swedish methadone maintenance program: A controlled study', *Drug and Alcohol Dependence*, 7, 249-256.

Haapanen, R. and Britton, L. (2002) 'Drug testing for youthful offenders on parole: An experimental evaluation', *Criminology and Public Policy*, 1(2), 217-244.

Harris, A. H., Gospodarevskaya, E., and Ritter, A. J. (2005) 'Randomised Trial of the Cost Effectiveness of Buprenorphine as an Alternative to Methadone Maintenance Treatment for Heroin Dependence in a Primary Care Setting', *PharmacoEconomics*, 23(1), 77-91.

Henggeler, S.W., Borduin, C.M., Melton, G.B., Mann, B.J., Smith, L.A., Hall, J.A., Cone, L., and Fucci, B.R. (1991) 'Effects of multisystemic therapy on drug use and abuse in serious juvenile offenders: a progress report from two outcome studies', *Family Dynamics of Addiction Quarterly*, 1(3), 40-51.

Hoffmann, N., and Miller, N. (1992) 'Treatment outcomes for abstinence-based programmes', *Psychiatric Annals*, 22(8), 402-408.

Hough, M., Clancy, A., McSweeney, T., and Turnbull, P.J. (2003) 'The impact of drug treatment and testing orders on offending: two year reconviction results', *Home Office Research Findings No. 184*, London: Home Office.

Hser, Y.I., Grella, C.E., Hubbard, R.L., Hsieh, S.C., Fletcher, B.W., Brown, B.S., and Anglin, M.D. (2001) 'An evaluation of drug treatments for adolescents in 4 US cities', *Archives of General Psychiatry*, 58, 689-695.

Hubbard, R.L., Craddock, S.G., Flynn, P.M., Anderson, J., and Etheridge, R.M. (1997) 'Overview of 1-year follow-up outcomes in the drug abuse treatment outcome study (DATOS)', *Psychology of Addictive Behaviours*, 11(4), 261-278.

Hubbard, R.L., Marsden, M.E., Rachal, J.V., Harwood, H.J., Cavanaugh, E.R., and Ginzburg, H.M. (1989) *Drug Abuse Treatment: A National Study of Effectiveness*, London: The University of North Carolina Press.

Hughey, R., and Klemke, L.W. (1996) 'Evaluation of a jail-based substance abuse treatment program', *Federal Probation*, 60(4), pp 40-44.

Hume, S., and Gorta, A. (1989) 'Effects of the NSW prison methadone programme on criminal recidivism and retention in methadone treatment', *Research Bulletin No. 19*, New South Wales, Australia: Department of Corrective Services.

Hutchinson, S.J., Taylor, A., Gruer, L., Barr, C., Mills, C., Elliott, L. Goldberg, D.J., Scott, R., and Gilchrist, G. (2000) 'One-year follow-up of opiate injectors treated with oral methadone in a GP-centred programme', *Addiction*, 95(7), 1055-1068.

Inciardi, J., Martin, S., Butzin, C., Hooper, R., and Harrison, L. (1997) 'An effective model of prison-based treatment for drug-involved offenders', *Journal of Drug Issues*, 27(2), 261-278.

Jason, L A., Olson, Bradley D., Ferrari, J.R., Majer, J.M., Alvarez, J., Stout, J. (2007) 'An examination of main and interactive effects of substance abuse recovery housing on multiple indicators of adjustment', *Addiction,* 102(7), 1114-1121.

Jones, P.R., and Goldkamp, J.S. (1993) 'Implementing pretrial drug-testing programmes in two experimental sites: some deterrence and jail bed implications', *The Prison Journal*, 73(2), 199-219.

Kinlock, T. W., Gordon, M. S., Schwartz, R. P., O'Grady, K. E (2008) 'A Study of Methadone Maintenance for Male Prisoners: 3-Month Postrelease Outcomes', *Criminal Justice and Behaviour*, 35(1), 34-47.

Knight, K., Simpson, D., Chatham, L., and Camacho, L. (1997) 'An assessment of prison-based drug treatment: Texas in-prison therapeutic community', *Journal of Offender Rehabilitation*, 24(3/4), 75-100.

Kosten, T.R., and Rounsaville, B.J. (1987) 'Sources of income as a predictor in opioid addicts: 2.5 year follow-up', National *Institute on Drug Abuse: Research Monograph Series*, 76, 196-199.

Krebs, C. P., Lindquist, C. H., Koetse, W., Lattimore, P. K. (2007) 'Assessing the long-term impact of drug court participation on recidivism with generalized estimating equations', *Drug and Alcohol Dependence*, 91(1), 57-68.

Lam, J.A., Jekel, J.F., Thompson, K.S., Leaf, P.J., Hartwell, S.W., and Florio, L. (1995) 'Assessing the value of a short-term residential drug treatment programme for homeless men', *Journal of Addictive Diseases*, 14(4), 21-39.

Latessa, E.J., and Moon, M.M. (1992) 'The effectiveness of acupuncture in an outpatient drug treatment program', *Journal of Contemporary Criminal Justice*, 8(4), 317-331.

Magura, S., Rosenblum, A., Lewis, C., and Joseph, H. (1993) 'The effectiveness of in-jail methadone maintenance', *The Journal of Drug Issues*, 23(1), p 75-99.

March, J. C., Oviedo-Joekes, E., Perea-Milla, E., Carrasco, F. (2006) 'Controlled trial of prescribed heroin in the treatment of opioid addiction', *Journal of Substance Abuse Treatment*, 31(2), 203-211.

Marlowe, D. B., Festinger, D.S., Dugosh, K. L., Lee, P.A. (2005) 'Are judicial status hearings a "key component" of drug court? Six and twelve months outcomes', *Drug and Alcohol Dependence*, 79 (2), 145-155.

Martin, S., and Scarpitti, F. (1993) 'An intensive case management approach for paroled IV drug users', *The Journal of Drug Issues*, 23(1), 43-59.

McBride, D.C., and Inciardi, J.A. (1993) 'The focused offender disposition program: philosophy, procedures, and preliminary findings', *Journal of Drug Issues, Winter*, 143-160.

McCusker, C. and Davies, M. (1996) 'Prescribing drug of choice to illicit heroin users: the experience of a UK community drug team', *Journal of Substance Abuse Treatment*, 13(6), 521-531.

McGlothlin, W., and Anglin, D. (1981) 'Long-term follow-up of clients of high- and low-dose methadone programmes', *Archives of General Psychiatry*, 38, 1055-1063.

McIvor, G. (2004) *Reconviction Following Drug Treatment and Testing Orders*. Edinburgh, United Kingdom: Scottish Executive Social Research.

McLellan, A.T., Arndt, I.O., Metzger, D.S., Woody, G.E., and O'Brien, C.P. (1993) 'The effects of psychosocial services in substance abuse treatment', *Journal of the American Medical Association*, 269, 1953-1959.

McSweeney, T., Stevens, A., Hunt, N. and Turnbull, P.J. (2007) 'Twisting arms or a helping hand?', *British Journal of Criminology*, 47, 470-490.

Messina, N.P., Wish, E.D., and Nemes, S. (1999) 'Therapeutic community treatment for substance abusers with antisocial personality disorder', *Journal of Substance Abuse Treatment*, 17(1-2), 121-128.

Metrebian, N., Shanahan, W., Stimson, G., Small, C., Lee, M., Mtutu, V., and Wells, B. (2001) 'Prescribing drug of choice to opiate dependent drug users: a comparison of clients receiving heroin with those receiving injectable methadone at a West London drug clinic', *Drug and Alcohol Review*, 20, 267-276.

Mitchell. O., and Herrell, A. (2006) 'Evaluation of the Breaking the Cycle Demonstration Project: Jacksonville, FL and Tacoma, WA', *Journal of Drug Issues*, 36(1), 97-118.

Naeem, F., Bhatti, F., Pickering, R., Kingdon, D. (2007) 'A controlled trial of the effectiveness of drug treatment & testing orders (DTTO) with standard care', *Journal of Substance Use*, 12(4), 253-265

Nemes, S., Wish, E., and Messina, N. (1999) 'Comparing the impact of standard and abbreviated treatment in a therapeutic community', *Journal of Substance Abuse Treatment*, 17(4), 339-347.

Payne, J. (2008) The Queensland Drug Court: a recidivism study of the first 100 graduates. Research and Public Policy Series No. 83. Canberra: Australian Institute of Criminology.

Perneger, T.V., Giner, F., del Rio M., and Mino A. (1998) 'Randomised trial of heroin maintenance programme for addicts who fail in conventional drug treatments', *British Medical Journal*, 317, 13-18.

Robertson, J. R., Raab, G. M., Bruce, M., McKenzie, J. S., Storkey, H. R., Salter, A. (2006) 'Addressing the efficacy of dihydrocodeine versus methadone as an alternative maintenance treatment for opiate dependence: A randomized controlled trial', *Addiction*, 101(12), 1752-1759.

Schwartz, R. P., Jaffe, J.H., Highfield, D. A., Callaman, J. M., O'Grady, K. E.(2007) 'A randomized controlled trial of interim methadone maintenance: 10-Month follow-up', *Drug and Alcohol Dependence*, 86(1), 30-36.

Simpson, D., Joe, G.W., and Brown, B.S. (1997) 'Treatment retention and follow-up outcomes in the drug abuse treatment outcome study (DATOS)', *Psychology of Addictive Behaviours*, 11(4), 294-307.

Simpson, D.D., and Sells, S.B. (1982) 'Effectiveness of treatment for drug abuse: an overview of the DARP research program', *Advances in Alcohol and Substance Abuse*, 2, 7-29.

Spohn, C., Piper, R.K., Martin, T., and Frenzel, E.D. (2001) 'Drug courts and recidivism: the results of an evaluation using two comparison groups and multiple indicators of recidivism', *Journal of Drug Issues*, 31(1), 149-176.

Strang, J., Marsden, J., Cummins, M., Farrell, M., Finch, E., Gossop, M., Stewart, D., and Welch, S. (2000) 'Randomized trial of supervised injectable versus oral methadone maintenance: report of feasibility and 6-month outcome', *Addiction*, 95(11), 1631-1645.

Taxman, F. S., Thanner, M. (2006) 'Risk, Need, and Responsivity (RNR): It All Depends', *Crime and Delinquency*, 52 (1), 28-51.

Teesson, M., Ross, J., Darke, S., Lynskey, M., Ali, R., Ritter, A., Cooke, R. (2006) 'One Year Outcomes for Heroin Dependence: Findings from the Australian Treatment Outcome Study (ATOS)', *Drug and Alcohol Dependence*, 83(2), 174-180.

Turner, S., Greenwood, P., Fain, T., and Deschenes, E. (1999) 'National Drug Court Institute review: perceptions of drug court: How offenders view ease of programme completion, strengths and weaknesses, and the impact on their lives,' *National Drug Court Review*, 2(1), 61-86.

Turner, S., Petersilia, J. and Deschenes, E.P. (1992) 'Evaluating intensive supervision probation/parole (ISP) for drug offenders', *Crime and Delinquency*, 38(4), 539-556.

Wexler, H., De Leon, G., Thomas, G., Kressel, D. and Peters, J. (1999) 'The Amity Prison TC evaluation', *Criminal Justice and Behaviour*, 26(2), 147-167.

Woody, G.E., McLellan, T., Luborsky, L., and O'Brien, C.P. (1987) 'Twelve-month follow-up of psychotherapy for opiate dependence', *American Journal of Psychiatry*, 144(5), 590-596.

Zhang, S. X. (2001) *An evaluation of the Los Angeles County Probation Juvenile Drug Treatment Boot Camp*, San Marcos, CA: California State University at San Marcos.

Other references

Farrington, D.P. and Petrosino, A. (2000) 'Systematic reviews of criminological interventions: The Campbell Collaboration Crime and Justice Group', *International Annals of Criminology*, 38, 49-66.

Farrington, D.P. and Welsh, B. (2002) 'Effects of improved street lighting on crime: a systematic review', *Home Office Research Study No. 251*. London: Home Office.

Farrington, D.P. (2003) 'Methodological quality standards for evaluation research', *Annals of the American Academy of Political and Social Science*, 583, 49-68.

Lipsey, M. W. and Wilson, D. B. (2001) *Practical Meta-Analysis*. Thousand Oaks, California: Sage.

Sherman, L.W., Denise Gottfredson, Doris MacKenzie, Peter Reuter, John Eck and Shawn Bushway (1997) *Preventing Crime: What Works, What Doesn't, What's Promising*, A Report to the U.S. Congress, Washington, D.C.: U.S. Department of Justice.

Welsh, B. and Farrington, D.P. (2002) 'Crime prevention effects of closed circuit television: a systematic review', *Home Office Research Study No. 252*. London: Home Office.

Appendix 1:

Measuring effect size

Post-Test Only Random Assignment Data
The OR used for analyzing post-test only data is different from the method of analysing before and after quasi-experimental data.

	Offender	Non-Offender
Experimental	a	b
Control	c	d

where a, b, c, d are numbers of people
OR = a*d/b*c

The null, or no effect, value of the OR is 1.0. To the extent that the OR exceeds 1.0, it might be concluded that the intervention was beneficial. To the extent that the OR falls below 1.0, it might be concluded that the intervention had negative effects.

The variance of the OR is calculated from its natural logarithm (LOR):

VAR (LOR) = 1/a + 1/b + 1/c +1/d

In order to produce a summary effect size in a meta-analysis, each effect size (here, LOR) is weighted by the inverse of its variance (1/V) in the fixed effects (FE) model.

Quasi-Experimental Data
For studies based on quasi-experimental designs, the OR was calculated from the natural logarithm of OR (LOR) using the formula below:

LOR = Ln (a2*d2/b2*c2) - Ln (a1*d1/b1*c1)

where a2, b2, c2, d2 are 'after' numbers of people and a1, b1, c1, d1 are 'before' numbers of people.

	Before intervention		After intervention	
	Non-offender	Offender	Non-offender	Offender
Experimental	a1	b1	a2	b2
Control	c1	d1	c2	d2

The variance of LOR is calculated using the following formula:

VAR (LOR) = 1/a1 + 1/b1 + 1/c1 + 1/d1 + 1/a2 + 1/b2 + 1/c2 + 1/d2

This method is based on comparing before and after ORs. This was considered preferable to only comparing after ORs as they do not control for pre-existing differences between the experimental and control groups. Because VLOR = VLORA + VLORB – covariance this formula overestimates VLOR. However, we cannot correct for the covariance because it is rarely reported. Therefore, our estimates of the statistical significance of effect sizes are conservative.

Other reports in this series

Closed-Circuit Television Surveillance and Crime Prevention
Authors: Brandon C. Welsh and David P. Farrington
A systematic review of the effects of closed circuit television surveillance based on 41 evaluations from five countries. Published in October 2007.
ISBN: 978-91-85664-79-5

Improved Street Lighting and Crime Prevention
Authors: David P. Farrington and Brandon C. Welsh.
A systematic review of the effects on crime of improved street lighting based on 13 evaluations from the United States and United Kingdom. Published in October 2007.
ISBN: 978-91-85664-78-8

Effectiveness of Neigbourhood Watch In Reducing Crime
Authors: Trevor H. Bennett, Katy R. Holloway, David P. Farrington
A systematic review of the effects of neighbourhood watch based on 36 evaluations. Published in March 2008.
ISBN: 978-91-85664-91-7

The Influence of Mentoring on Reoffending
Authors: Darrick Jolliffe and David P. Farrington
A rapid evidence assessment of the effects of mentoring based on 18 evaluations. Published in March 2008.
ISBN: 978-91-85664-90-0

Effects of Early Family/Parent Training Programs on Antiscocial Behavior & Delinquency
Authors: Alex R. Piquero, David P. Farrington, Brandon C. Welsh, Richard Tremblay and Wesley G. Jennings.
A systematic review of effects of early family/parent training based on 55 evaluations. Published in June 2008.
ISBN: 978-91-85664-95-5

Effectiveness of Programmes to Reduce School Bullying
Authors: Maria M. Ttofi, David P. Farrington, Anna C. Baldry
A systematic review of the effectiveness of anti-bullying programmes based on 59 evaluations. Published in October 2008.
ISBN:978-91-86027-11-7

The reports can be ordered from:
Fritzes Kundservice, 106 47 Stockholm, Sweden
Phone: + 46 (0)8 690 91 90, fax: + 46(0)8 690 91 91,
e-mail: order.fritzes@nj.se